Making Spelling Sense™

By:
Bonnie Terry, M.Ed.

Third Printing 2004
Printed in the United States of America
ISBN 1-891106-02-3

Also by Bonnie Terry:

Educational Games:

The Sentence Zone™ A Sentence Building Game
It makes learning English grammar easy and fun. For grades 1 through 12. Six levels of play, from simple to complex. An instructive and enjoyable way to learn English grammar!

The Comprehension Zone™: Rocket Rap™ A Comprehension and Study Skills Game
Game cuts learning time while improving reading comprehension. Three levels of play: 2nd-3rd grades, 4th-6th grades, 7th-12th grades.

The Math Zone™ A Math Card Game
It builds basic math skills while having fun. Includes two decks: 7-9 years, 9 years-adult.

Super Spacers™ A Perfect Math and Spelling Paper Organizer
Place 10 problems or words on a page, evenly spaced out -- No more messy papers!

Books:

Making Spelling Sense™
Learn how to spell over 500 of the most frequently-used words in the English language.
Incorporates visual, auditory, and tactile modes of learning. It is phonetically- and sequentially-based.

Making Spelling Sense II™
A step beyond spelling the 500 most frequently-used words in the English language. Contains: prefixes, suffixes, root words, word origins and much more!
Incorporates visual, auditory, and tactile modes of learning. It is phonetically- and sequentially-based.

Five Minutes to Better Reading Skills™
A Fun, Fast, Phonic Approach to Improve Reading Skills (Second Edition)
Only five minutes of reading drills daily will improve reading; makes faster, smoother and more confident readers.

Ten Minutes to Better Study Skills™
A Fun, Fast Approach to Improve Writing and Study Skills
The complete book of study guides and pre-writing forms. Makes homework, note taking, paragraph and essay writing easier.

Writers Easy Reference Guide™
This easy reference guide contains those all-important references you need when writing: synonyms, transition words, bibliography information, capitalization rules, punctuation rules, letter writing, and much much more. It conveniently fits into your notebook.

Copyright © 2004, 1996 Bonnie Terry
Printed in the United States of America
Third Printing 2004
ISBN 1-891106-02-3

Available from:
Bonnie Terry Learning • 238 Poet Smith Drive • Auburn, CA 95603 • (530) 888-7160
www.bonnieterrylearning.com -- or -- e-mail: info@bonnieterrylearning.com

Acknowledgement

The author wishes to thank Patricia Terry for her contributions. She wishes to thank Dick, Rick, and Nick for their inspiration and patience throughout the creation of this book. The author wishes to thank Doreen Wood and Lynda Young for their editing.

Welcome to *Making Spelling Sense*^{TM}*!*

Making Spelling Sense^{TM} comes from my 30⁺ years of teaching both regular education and special education students in regular classes, special day classes, and resource classes.

With **Making Spelling Sense**^{TM}, you will learn how to spell over 500 of the most frequently used words in the English language. You will learn this in a step-by-step method that makes sense to you, and from this knowledge, you will be able to spell thousands more words.

The method utilized in **Making Spelling Sense**^{TM} is one that **incorporates visual, auditory, and tactile modes of learning. It is phonetically and sequentially based.** It also strengthens visual perception through the puzzles and other exercises that are provided.

The whole point of **Making Spelling Sense**^{TM} is to make spelling make sense to everyone. There is an actual structure to our language, and if we teach spelling according to the structure, everyone can spell.

There are several important ideas that must be shared with you from the start.

* *   There are two types of letters, consonants and vowels. In order to have a word, you must have a combination of vowels and consonants. Two words (*I* and *a*) are made of vowels only. *Vowels are the letters that give **voice** or **personality** to our words.* Without the vowels, all you have are letters next to each other, that don't make any sense.

* *   There are **eight basic spelling patterns** in the English language and within some of the patterns, there are sub-groups.

* *   There are a few words that must be learned by **sight** since they don't follow the patterns.

* *   We do have some special letters:
  The Borrowers 'c' and **'g'**, and some **Silent Letters**.

The Book:
> Consists of **50 spelling lessons** for the **500 most used words** in the English language.

The Appendix:
> **Practice Test Sheets**
> **Rules for Suffixes, Open and Closed Syllables, and Prefixes**

Table of Contents
Eight Spelling Patterns

The Sight Words and words ending with a 'v' sound are introduced now. There are a few sight words that are commonly used in simple sentences that we don't want to mispell.

There are 24 sub-groups in this pattern. They are:

ee	ēe
oa	ōa,
oo	ōo, oo
ai & ay	āi, āy
ea	ea (ir), ea (ā), ea (ē), ea (ĕ), ea (ur),
au	au (ô), au (ă),
ou	ou (ou), ou (ōo), ou (oo), ou (ō), ou (ô), ou (ŭ), ou (ôr)
oi & oy	oi(oi), oy(oi),
ie	ie (ē), ie (ī)

Procedure for introducing each lesson:

1. Go over the spelling pattern and give an example.

2. Post the spelling words and their patterns either on the board or bulletin board so that students can see them all week long. Just cover them up or erase them when it is test time. Posting the words for the students to see every time they look at the front of the room further impresses on their brain the corect way of spelling the words, as well as gives the spelling pattern association to them. This process is called 'neuro-impress'. You might also want to begin a list on the board that will cover the eight spelling patterns. Add each pattern to it as you learn it.

3. Students copy the words and patterns next to them.

4. Students do the fill-in-the-blanks and/or puzzles.

5. Pass out copies of the practice/test sheet. (Be sure to use the correct Lesson sheet; the sheets are to be used for practice tests.) See appendix.

6. Follow the pretest procedure on the next page.

7. You may want to do additional activities with your words such as having the students use their list words in sentences or in a story.

8. Give a final test on regular sheet of paper.

Procedure for doing the pretest:

1. Remind the students which vowel pattern you are working with.

2. Give each word, a sound at a time. The students write each sound down in the first column as you say the sound.

3. After you have said the sounds of the whole word, the students say the word and they write it again, in the second column.

4. Students write the vowel pattern in the third column.

5. Students are to fold their papers on the dotted line. Then, with only the fourth column facing them, they are to write their words as you say them back to them.

6. Students are to unfold their papers and check their words.

7. Be sure to do both a pretest test and a final test, to be sure the students have retained the concept and spelling of the words. You may want to do the lesson one day, pretest the next day, and the final test on the third day. You may also do the lesson and pretest on the same day, but do the final test on another day, to be sure you have retention.

8. *Optional:* On the back of the pretest, give one or two sentences as dictation. If you do this, say the whole sentence, then repeat it, a phrase at a time. Repeat it as many times as necessary, so all students hear it and have a chance to write it. You can use sentences from the fill in the blank exercises or make up your own.

Making Spelling Sense I

Bonnie Terry, M.Ed.

Lesson One - V̆C Vowel/Consonant Pattern

This is the first pattern, and it is the easiest one to master. Remember that we have two types of letters, consonants and vowels. The vowels act as the *'star'* of the word. You can't have a word without a vowel. If you don't have any vowels, all you have are letters next to each other. In order to have a word, you need a vowel, or *'star'*. You might think of it in terms of your favorite television program. You need some *'stars'* or actors in order to have the program.

When you have a word in the Vowel/Consonant Pattern (v̆c), you have one vowel, *'star,'* next to a consonant. The vowel gives its short sound (˘). You can also refer to the short sound as its nickname since a vowel usually gives either its name sound (long sound) or its nickname (short sound).

* Remember, the vowel patterns start at the first vowel in each word part (syllable). You can have none, one, two, or three beginning sounds for each syllable, then the vowel pattern. (For example, in the word 'in' there is no beginning consonant, so the *vowel/consonant pattern* starts immediately; <u>c</u>ap, *'c' is the beginning sound and 'ap' is the vowel/consonant pattern*; <u>tr</u>ap *'tr' are the beginning sounds and 'ap' is the vowel/consonant pattern*, <u>str</u>ap, *'str' are the beginning sounds and 'ap' is the vowel/ consonant pattern*).

v̆c	words	pattern
it		
and		
in		
is		
that *		
of **		
on		
as		
wish *		
his		

*Sometimes two letters come together to make a new sound. The *'th'* comes together and makes either a noisy *'th'* like in *this, that,* and *the,* or a quiet sound like in *'thumb'*. When the *'sh'* comes together, you do not hear the *'s'* and the *'h'* sound separately; instead you hear the *'sh'* sound.

**The *'f'* in *'of '* is giving the noisy *'v'* sound. You make the same movement with your mouth for both letters, the *'v'* is noisy and the *'f'* is *usually* quiet.

2

Find the following sentence in the puzzle:

example:

It is his.

i	b	d	t
t	i	c	a
i	s	t	p
d	h	i	s

It is on that.

i	c	d	t
t	b	e	a
i	s	c	h
a	o	n	t

Fill in the blanks using words from the list.

of   and   in   is   that   it   on   as   with   his

1. His hat _____ on that.

2. His cat and hat are _____ that.

3. The bat is with _____ big ball.

4. That is _____ bat.

5. Ben came _____ his hat.

6. That cat is _____ big as that dog.

7. Mat sits _____ front of him.

8. Sam has one _____ his caps with him.

9. Kim _____ Sam came back.

10. The frog did _____!

Lesson Two - ĬC Vowel/Consonant Pattern Continued

When you have a Vowel/Consonant Pattern (ĭc), the vowel gives its short sound (ĭ). You can also refer to this as its nickname since a vowel usually gives either its name sound (long sound) or its nickname (short sound).

ĭc	words	patterns
if		
up		
them *		
then *		
into		
has		
him		
than *		
its		
did		

*Sometimes two letters come together to make a new sound. The 'th' comes together and makes either a noisy 'th' like in *this, that,* and *the,* or a quiet sound like in *'thumb'*.

Find the sentence in the puzzle.

example:

It is his.

i	b	d	t
t	i	c	a
i	s	t	p
d	h	i	s

Did it see them?

a	d	h	e
b	i	t	m
i	d	e	c
t	s	e	d

Fill in the blanks using words from your list.

if up them then into has him than its did

1. Did Tim see _____?

2. Kim's cat is _____ in the tree.

3. That black cat _____ white spots on it.

4. I _____ it!

5. Sam sat with _____.

6. Ben likes the red pen better _____ the blue pen.

7. Dad got his hat and _____ left.

8. Bob ran _____ the cave.

9. Tod wants to see _____ he can go with me.

10. The cat sits in _____ bed.

Lesson Three - V̆C Vowel/Consonant Pattern Continued

When you have a Vowel/Consonant Pattern **(v̆c)**, the vowel gives its short sound **(v̆)**. You can also refer to this as its nickname since a vowel usually gives either its name sound (long sound) or its nickname (short sound).

v̆c	words	patterns
men		
big		
set		
last		
us		
left		
end		
next		
asked*		

*The *'ed'* suffix has three different sounds. Sometimes it will give the *'d'* sound (mailed); sometimes it will give the *'t'* sound (asked); and sometimes it will give the *'ed'* sound (hunted).

6

Find the sentence in the puzzle.

The big men asked him.

example:

It is his.

i	b	d	t
t	i	c	a
i	s	t	p
d	h	i	s

d	e	g	t
h	k	f	h
i	s	e	e
m	a	n	b
b	a	e	i
c	d	m	g

Find all of the words from this list in the word search.

men big set last us left end next asked

a	s	k	e	d	l	b
l	e	f	t	i	a	i
a	t	e	n	d	s	g
s	g	h	e	u	t	m
t	d	f	x	s	a	e
w	a	n	t	c	b	n

Lesson Four - ᵥ̆C Vowel/Consonant Pattern Continued

When you have a Vowel/Consonant Pattern **(v̆c)**, the vowel gives its short sound **(v̆)**. You can also refer to this as its nickname since a vowel usually gives either its name sound (long sound) or its nickname (short sound).

v̆c	words	patterns
red		
fish *		
plants		
black **		
run		
front		
sad		
lived		
add		
yet		

*Sometimes two letters come together to make a new sound. When the *'sh'* comes together, you do not hear the *'s'* and the *'h'* sound separately; instead you hear the *'sh'* sound.

**When a short vowel word ends with the *'k'* sound, it is always spelt with a *'ck'*. The two letter spelling of the *'k'* sound keeps the vowel protected so it can give its short sound *(ex. back vs. bake, pick vs. pike)*.

Find this sentence in the puzzle:

The fish is black and red.

example: It is on that

i	c	d	t
t	b	e	a
i	s	c	h
a	o	n	t

t	a	f	e	c	k	h
h	b	c	d	a	a	d
e	s	h	i	l	n	e
f	i	g	s	b	d	r

Fill in the blanks using words from your list.

red   fish   plants   black   run   front   sad   lived   add   yet

1. The _____ fish swim in the pond.

2. The trees and _____ are _____ and green.

3. Tim will _____ some _____ to the pond.

4. The big frog _____ with the fish in the pond.

5. Did he go home _____ ?

6. Sam was _____ to see Nick sick.

7. Ben will _____ to the _____ of the park.

9

Lesson Five - V̌C Vowel/Consonant Pattern Continued

When you have a Vowel/Consonant Pattern (v̌c), the vowel gives its short sound (v̌). You can also refer to this as its nickname since a vowel usually gives either its name sound (long sound) or its nickname (short sound).

v̌c	words	patterns
at		
this *		
from		
had		
not		
but		
when **		
can		
an		
which **		

*Sometimes two letters come together to make a new sound. The 'th' comes together and makes either a noisy 'th' like in *this, that,* and *the,* or a quiet sound like in *'thumb'*.

**When the 'wh' comes together, you do not hear the 'w' and the 'h' sound separately; instead you hear the 'hw' sound. When the 'ch' comes together, you do not hear the 'c' and the 'h' sound separately; instead you hear the 'ch' sound.

10

example: Did it see them?

His am at (Did) sat spot cat up them has see me in (it) that (see) into add just lot from this (them) on him in (?)

Find the sentence in the puzzle.

Did she get this from that can?

Did can she come pie lamp get front

if last this land is but if and then of

west from add let much this that an

fat up from it can an which land bit?

Find all of the words from this list in the word search.

at this from had not but when can an which

w	a	t	b	c	b	f
h	c	h	a	d	u	r
e	a	i	n	o	t	o
n	n	s	d	e	f	m
h	w	h	i	c	h	g

Lesson Six - V̆C Vowel/Consonant Pattern Continued

When you have a Vowel/Consonant Pattern **(v̆c)** , the vowel gives its short sound **(v̆)** . You can also refer to this as its nickname since a vowel usually gives either its name sound (long sound) or its nickname (short sound).

v̆c	words	patterns
just		
get		
back *		
much **		
man		
must		
such **		
help		
off		
went		

*When a short vowel word ends with the *'k'* sound, it is always spelt with a *'ck'*. The two letter spelling of the *'k'* sound keeps the vowel protected so it can give its short sound *(ex. back vs. bake, pick vs. pike)*.

**Sometimes two letters come together to make a new sound. When the *'ch'* comes together, you do not hear the *'c'* and the *'h'* sound separately; instead you hear the *'ch'* sound.

Find this sentence in the puzzle:

example: Did it see them?

His am at (Did) sat spot cat
up them has see me in (it)
that (see) into add just lot
from this (them) on him in (?)

The man must get back.

A	to	nap	The	is	this	up	set	fast	fin	help
mug	dad	sad	the	must	lived	it	man	off		
such	mit	at	of	land	add	must	big	mat	red	
went	from	but	left	get	plants	on	yet	had		
just	his	best	into	as	them	back	six	.		

Fill in the blanks using words from your list.

just back get much man must such help off went

1. This is _____ a help.

2. Your dad _____ help that _____.

3. Kim was a big _____ to me.

4. The bug must _____ _____ of the frog.

5. Ted _____ home to tend the plants.

6. The man _____ got _____ from his trip.

7. Did you see how _____ pie he ate?

Lesson Seven - ✓C Vowel/Consonant Pattern Continued

When you have a Vowel/Consonant Pattern (v̆c) , the vowel gives its short sound (v̆) . You can also refer to this as its nickname since a vowel usually gives either its name sound (long sound) or its nickname (short sound).

v̆c	words	patterns
land		
got		
hand		
let		
best		
it's *		
sun		
top		
didn't *		
cut		

*You have two words in your list that are contractions: **it's** and **didn't**. Contractions are words that have combined two other words by dropping one of the letters out, for example: **it is** becomes **it's**; **did not** becomes **didn't**.

Find all of the words from this list in the word search:

land got hand let best it's sun top didn't cut

t	o	p	h	l	g
c	u	t	a	e	o
d	s	u	n	t	t
l	a	n	d	a	i
d	i	d	n	't	t
b	e	s	t	s	's

Fill in the blanks with words from this list:

land got hand let best it's sun top didn't cut

1. She _____ her _____ .

2. _____ the best _____ to grow plants.

3. Nick _____ want to go to the _____ of

   the hill.

4. He saved the _____ for last.

5. Rick _____ to go to see the _____

   come up.

6. Dad _____ Nick go with him.

Lesson Eight - V̆C Vowel/Consonant Pattern Continued

When you have a Vowel/Consonant Pattern (v̆c), the vowel gives its short sound (v̆). You can also refer to this as its nickname since a vowel usually gives either its name sound (long sound) or its nickname (short sound).

v̆c	words	patterns
less		
dog		
rest		
six		
yes		
ran		
hot		
list		
ten		

Find the sentence in the puzzle.

Six is less than ten.

example: It is on that.

i	c	d	t
t	b	e	a
i	s	c	h
a	o	n	t

a	c	d	s
n	t	s	i
n	h	s	x
e	a	e	i
t	n	l	s

Find all of the words from this list in the word search:

less	wind	dog	rest	six	yes	ran	hot	list	ten

a	b	l	e	s	s	f
c	w	i	n	d	i	t
r	e	s	t	o	x	e
a	d	t	w	g	w	n
n	y	e	s	h	o	t

Lesson Nine - V̆C Vowel/Consonant Pattern Continued

When you have a Vowel/Consonant Pattern (v̆c), the vowel gives its short sound (v̆). You can also refer to this as its nickname since a vowel usually gives either its name sound (long sound) or its nickname (short sound).

v̆c	words	patterns
fast		
kept		
can't *		
stand		
box		
that's **		
class		
stop		
am		
past		

You have two words in your list that are contractions: **can't** and **that's**. Contractions are words that have combined two other words by dropping one of the letters out, for example: **can not** becomes **can't**; **that is** becomes **that's**.

**Sometimes two letters come together to make a new sound. The *'th'* comes together and makes either a noisy *'th'* like in *this, that,* and *the,* or a quiet sound like in *'thumb'*.

Find this sentence in the puzzle:

I can't stand on the box.

example:

It is on that.

i	c	d	t
t	b	e	a
i	s	c	h
a	o	n	t

a	b	j	k	h	e	n
i	c	i	h	t	b	m
c	d	e	g	n	o	x
a	s	t	f	o	p	r
n	't	a	n	d	q	s

Fill in the blanks from your word list.

fast	kept	can't	stand	box	that's	class	stop	am	past

1. The big man went _____ the box.

2. Red is for _____ , and green is for go.

3. Kim _____ go home yet.

4. See the _____ the _____ left us.

5. _____ the fish the class _____ .

6. I _____ a _____ runner.

7. You can _____ up any time now.

Lesson Ten - ĬC Vowel/Consonant Pattern Continued

When you have a Vowel/Consonant Pattern (ĭc) , the vowel gives its short sound (ĭ) . You can also refer to this as its nickname since a vowel usually gives either its name sound (long sound) or its nickname (short sound).

ĭc	words	patterns
ship*		
fact		
sat		
miss		
glass		
rock **		
check **		
map		
job		

*Sometimes two letters come together to make a new sound. When the 'sh' comes together, you do not hear the 's' and the 'h' sound separately; instead you hear the 'sh' sound. When the 'ch' comes together, you do not hear the 'c' and the 'h' sound separately; instead you hear the 'ch' sound.

**When a short vowel word ends with the 'k' sound, it is always spelt with a 'ck'. The two letter spelling of the 'k' sound keeps the vowel protected so it can give its short sound *(ex. back vs. bake, pick vs. pike)*.

Find the sentence in the puzzle:

The ship will rock the glass.

e	s	c	c	k	g	k
h	h	d	o	t	h	l
t	i	e	r	h	i	s
a	p	l	l	e	j	s
b	w	i	f	g	l	a

example:

It is on that.

i	c	d	t
t	b	e	a
i	s	c	h
a	o	n	t

Find all of the words from this list in the word search:

| ship | fact | sat | miss | glass | rock | check | map | job |

a	g	l	a	s	s
c	h	e	c	k	h
f	a	c	t	b	i
j	o	b	m	a	p
r	o	c	i	c	d
r	o	c	s	a	t
e	f	g	s	h	i
r	o	c	k	j	k

2-syllable (ŭc) words: both syllables have the (ŭc) pattern

ŭc/ŭc	words	patterns
bottom (ŭc/ŭc)		
second (ŭc/ŭc)		
seven (ŭc/ŭc)		
upon (ŭc/ŭc)		
cannot (ŭc/ŭc)		
happen (ŭc/ŭc)		
common (ŭc/ŭc)		
hundred (ŭc/ŭc)*		
often (ŭc/ŭc)**		
sentence (ŭc/ŭc, ⓔ c=s)***		

* Remember, the vowel patterns start at each vowel, You can have one, two, or three beginning sounds for each syllable, then the vowel pattern. (_c_ap, _tr_ap, _str_ap), so _h_un _dr_ed is a vc/vc pattern with the **un** the first vc pattern and **ed** the second vc pattern.

**In some parts of the country, the _'t'_ in _'often'_ is silent.

***When the letters _'c'_ and _'g'_ are followed by an _'e, i, or y',_ they go _'soft'._
The _'c'_ gives the _'s'_ sound and the _'g'_ gives the _'j'_ sound. We indicate it next to the spelling pattern like this.

ⓔ   ⓘ   ⓨ   ⓔ   ⓘ   ⓨ   For more on this, see page 94.
c=s   c=s   c=s   g=j   g=j   g=j

Find the sentence in the puzzle:

example:

It is on that.

i	c	d	t
t	b	e	a
i	s	c	h
a	o	n	t

He cannot often see himself.

a	b	c	e	n	l	f
e	c	d	t	s	e	l
h	a	e	f	h	e	e
f	n	t	o	i	h	s
g	n	o	j	k	i	m

Fill in the blanks from your word list.

often   seven   cannot   common   bottom
second   upon   hundred   happen   sentence

1. The man sees a _____ fish.

2. It is not _____ to clap all day long.

3. The fish are on the _____ of the river.

4. The man is _____ the box.

5. It is the _____ one.

6. Did you _____ to see them last night?

7. Tom _____ go by himself.

8. She _____ runs to the store.

9. Sam has _____ red hats.

10. This is the last _____ on this page.

Lesson Twelve - (V̄CE̸)Vowel/Consonant/Silent E̸ Pattern

In the v̄ce̸ pattern, the **magic** or **evil e** takes over. The shape of the **e** is that of a curled up snake. The other vowels are afraid of the snake, so when it asks a vowel its name, the vowel is afraid to give its nickname (short sound). Instead it gives its actual name, its long sound, and the e̸ remains silent.

v̄ce̸	words	patterns
these		
like		
time		
make*		
made		
use		
write		
same		
came		
place ** e̸ (c=s)		

*When a short vowel word ends with the 'k' sound, it is always spelt with a 'ck'. The two letter spelling of the 'k' sound keeps the vowel protected so it can give its short sound (ex. back vs. bake, pick vs. pike).

**When the letters 'c' and 'g' are followed by an 'e, i, or y', they go 'soft'. The 'c' gives the 's' sound and the 'g' gives the 'j' sound. For more on this, see page 94.   e̸ (c=s)   i (c=s)   y (c=s)   e̸ (g=j)   i (g=j)   y (g=j)

Find the sentence in the puzzle.

example:

The man made these plants.

It is on that.

i	c	d	t
t	b	e	a
i	s	c	h
a	o	n	t

i	f	t	e	l	a
h	g	h	d	p	n
m	n	e	c	e	t
a	a	m	b	s	s
d	e	t	h	e	a

Fill in the blanks from your word list.

place   use   make   like   write   these   time   same   came   made

1. The man will _____ the same ball he did before.

2. Fish _____ to swim.

3. Did Rick _____ these words?

4. The dog came to the _____ .

5. The men _____ a hundred toy fish.

6. _____ books are mine.

7. Ken got here on _____ .

8. Mom _____ over to help _____ the cake.

9. Are we going to do the _____ thing today?

Lesson Thirteen - (V̄CE̸) Vowel/Consonant/Silent E̸ Continued

In the v̄ce̸ pattern, the **magic** or **evil e** takes over. The shape of the **e** is that of a curled up snake. The other vowels are afraid of the snake, so when it asks a vowel its name, the vowel is afraid to give its nickname (short sound). Instead it gives its actual its long sound, and the e̸ remains silent.

v̄ce̸	words	patterns
take*		
name		
line		
while**		
those**		
side		
life		
page*** ⓔ g=j		
whole**		

*When a short vowel word ends with the 'k' sound, it is always spelt with a 'ck'. The two letter spelling of the 'k' sound keeps the vowel protected so it can give its short sound (ex. back vs. bake, pick vs. pike).

**When the 'wh' comes together, you do not hear the 'w' and the 'h' sound separately; instead you usually hear the 'hw' sound. There are a few exceptions to this, when the 'w' remains silent as in 'whole', 'who', and 'whose'.

***When the letters 'c' and 'g' are followed by an 'e, i, or y', they go 'soft'. The 'c' gives the 's' sound and the 'g' gives the 'j' sound. For more on this, see page 94.   ⓔ c=s   ⓘ c=s   ⓨ c=s   ⓔ g=j   ⓘ g=j   ⓨ g=j

Find the sentence in the puzzle.

example:

I will take the whole page.

It is on that.

i	c	d	t
t	b	e	a
i	s	c	h
a	o	n	t

a	b	i	c	n	o
t	e	w	d	l	m
h	k	i	e	j	k
e	a	l	f	g	e
w	t	l	p	a	i
h	o	l	e	g	h

Find all of the words from this list in the word search:

take   name   line   while   those   side   life   page   whole

w	i	e	k	l	i	v	e	n	t
h	g	h	l	i	n	e	s	n	t
o	e	f	s	f	o	n	q	a	h
l	c	d	i	e	n	p	e	m	o
e	a	b	d	l	t	a	k	e	s
p	a	g	e	m	w	h	i	l	e

Lesson Fourteen - (V̄CE̸) Vowel/Consonant/Silent E̸ Pattern Continued

In the v̄ce̸ pattern, the **magic** or **evil e** takes over. The shape of the **e** is that of a curled up snake. The other vowels are afraid of the snake, so when it asks a vowel its name, the vowel is afraid to give its nickname (short sound). Instead it gives its actual name, its long sound, and the e̸ remains silent.

v̄ce̸	words	patterns
five		
late		
face * ⓔ c=s		
gave		
space * ⓔ c=s		
close		
ate		
state		
fine		
ice * ⓔ c=s		

*When the letters 'c' and 'g' are followed by an 'e, i, or y', they go 'soft'. The 'c' gives the 's' sound and the 'g' gives the 'j' sound. For more on this, see page 94.   ⓔ c=s   ⓘ c=s   ⓨ c=s   ⓔ g=j   ⓘ g=j   ⓨ g=j

Find the sentence in the puzzle:

The man gave his space up.

example:

It is his.

i	b	d	t
t	i	c	a
i	s	t	p
d	h	i	s

t	e	h	i	p	a	c
h	t	e	s	s	c	e
e	a	v	c	s	d	u
m	l	a	v	i	e	p
a	n	g	e	h	f	j

Find all of the words from this word list in the word search.

ate   late   face   gave   space   close   state   fine   ice

a	b	s	p	a	c	e	g	f
s	t	a	t	e	s	c	a	i
d	e	f	n	o	g	h	v	r
i	f	i	l	a	t	e	e	e
k	i	c	l	o	s	e	n	o
p	n	e	v	i	w	c	x	y
r	e	v	f	a	c	e	z	a

Lesson Fifteen - (V̄CE̸) Vowel/Consonant/Silent E̸ Pattern Continued

In the v̄ce̸ pattern, the **magic** or **evil e** takes over. The shape of the **e** is that of a curled up snake. The other vowels are afraid of the snake, so when it asks a vowel its name, the vowel is afraid to give its nickname (short sound). Instead it gives its actual name, its long sound, and the e̸ remains silent.

*Once upon a time there was a queen who lived in a far off kingdom. She knew that 'king' began with a **'k'** which has points on it, just like the king's crown. She was upset because 'queen' in those days was spelled 'qeen.' She wanted something special by her first letter. She thought and thought and asked everyone in the kingdom what they thought. One day a little boy came to her with a special gift. He knew she was upset about 'qeen', so he made her a headband of flowers to cheer her up. The queen liked the headband so much that she decided to put a **'u'** after the **'q'** in her name, since the **'u'** was the same shape as the headband. Everyone in the kingdom was happy with the new way of spelling 'queen.' They liked it so much they decided to place a **'u'** after every **'q'** from then on. And that is why you never see a **'q'** without a **'u'** following it.*

v̄ce̸	words	patterns
quite (v̄ce̸) Since the u always follows the q, it is not part of the vowel pattern.		
size (v̄ce̸)		
wide (v̄ce̸)		
states (v̄ce̸)		
cake (v̄ce̸)		
2 Syllables **inside** (v̆c/v̄ce̸)		
complete (v̆c/v̄ce̸) *		

* Remember, the vowel patterns start at each vowel, You can have one, two, or three beginning sounds for each syllable, then the vowel pattern. (*c*ap, *tr*ap, *str*ap)

Find this sentence in the puzzle:

Example:

The cake is quite wide.

It is his.

i	b	d	t
t	i	c	a
i	s	t	p
d	h	i	s

e	k	t	a	b	d	e
i	a	h	i	t	i	e
s	c	e	u	w	i	d
q	u	i	t	e	d	g

Fill in the blanks using the words from your list.

inside   states   quite   size   complete   wide   cake

1.   Did you see the _____ of that huge glass?

2.   _____ the page.

3.   The ship is big _____.

4.   Mom baked the _____ for my birthday.

5.   The dog is _____ big.

6.   I have lived in three _____.

7.   That door is extra _____.

Lesson Sixteen - Sight Words

There are 17 sight words in the list of the 500 most used words in the English language. Within these sight words there are some similarities that must be noted. For instance, people always say, "Why aren't 'have', 'love', 'dove', 'above' and 'live' pronounced with the long vowel sounds? After all, there is a **silent e** ." There is a story or legend about those words that end with the **'v'** sound.

*Many, many years ago, during the Roman times, scribes were sent from king to king to deliver messages that they wrote on scrolls. Now, sometimes these messages had to be sent quickly, so they were written while the scribe was travelling. The scribe would bring the scroll to the other kings after several days of travel. Often the king wasn't sure what word was written because the letters **'u'** and **'v'** were so close in shape. One day, one of the kings decided to put an end to this problem by saying, "From now on, if a **'v'** is at the end of the word, put an **'e'** after it. Then I will know if it is a **'v'** or a **'u'**." And that has been the way of the letter **'v'** ever since. The letter **'v'** never ends a word by itself. With that in mind, the words 'have,' 'above,' 'dove,' 'love,' and 'live' actually follow the v̆c pattern because the final **silent e** is there to **denote** that the letter is a **'v'** and not a **'u'**.*

sight	words	patterns
the		sight
does		
kind		
find		
mind		
have (v̆c)		
above (v́/v̆c)*		
love (v̆c)		
dove (v̆c)		
live (v̆c)		

32

For more on the v́ pattern, see pages 82, 90, 92, or appendix page 20.

Fill your words in the story:

love above does dove mind kind

Tom falls in _____ with Jenny after she gives him a

_____. The dove flies _____ his home.

Tom _____ not _____ it because the dove flies

back to him all the time. The dove likes Tom. Tom is _____

to him. He feeds him and takes good care of him.

Find your other words and circle them in the puzzle:

the find dove have live

here	(the)	apple	will	find	cute	see	there	time
fast	have	glass	cut	dove	live	job	map	the
stand	box	find	miss	rock	map	live	can't	have
take	live	wide	the	often	himself	done	happen	

sight	words	patterns

sight		
one		sight
done		
some		
come		
what		
most		
both		
oh		
want		
2 Syllables someone		

Sight Words Continued

Fill in the blanks with your words:

| one   someone   come   both   want |

The classes had to find _____ to _____ give
them lunch. _____man came to _____ classes
with lunch for them. The classes _____ to thank him.

Find your list words here.

| one   some   come   someone   what   done   most   both   oh |

s	o	m	e	o	n	e	d
m	o	s	t	b	h	w	o
o	h	c	o	m	a	h	n
b	o	t	h	e	t	a	e
c	o	m	e	o	h	t	s
s	o	m	e	s	o	n	e

Lesson Eighteen - VV (Vowel/Vowel Patterns)

There are 23 sub-groups of **vowel/vowel** patterns. The words will be divided into their sub-groups for easier learning and easier spelling. In most of the sub-groups, the two vowels combine to make new sounds. However, four of the sub-groups follow the same rule:

When two vowels go walking, the first one does the talking (says its name), and the second one is silent.

v̄v long ē	words	patterns
keep		
need		
screen		
leaves*		
least		
spears		
peak		
cream		
please		
2 Syllables between (v́/v̄v̄)**		
either (v̄v̄/v + r)		
people (v̄v̄/c + le)		
easy (v̄v̄/v́)**		

*When you make a word that ends in an 'f' plural, you drop the 'f' and add 'ves' (leaf to leaves).
**For more on the v́ pattern, see pages 82, 90, 92, or appendix page 20.*

Find your list words in the puzzle:

| keep need screen leaves least spears peak |
| cream please between either people easy |

a	b	n	c	l	s	p	e	a	r	s	c	g	h
k	e	e	p	e	p	e	p	l	e	a	s	e	e
c	r	e	a	m	e	o	p	e	a	k	s	i	a
c	d	d	v	i	a	p	p	a	u	y	e	t	s
s	c	r	e	e	n	l	r	v	v	z	f	h	y
l	e	a	s	t	k	e	b	e	t	w	e	e	n
e	f	g	h	j	l	m	t	s	w	a	b	r	i

Fill in the blanks with words from your list.

| easy keep need spears leaves people please |

   A dog, a man, and a fish live on a ship. To live on a ship is not_____.
The man on the ship does not see the _____ of trees very often. The
ship will _____ wind to go. The man must _____ the
_____ near by so he can spear sharks. The man wishes for fresh cream.
He asks _____ to _____ send some dry food before the
storm comes. Between the dog and the fish, life is fun. The man is not sad.

Lesson Nineteen - VV (Vowel/Vowel Patterns) Continued

When two vowels go walking, the first one does the talking (says its name), and the second one is silent.

v̄v̶ long ō	words	patterns
soap		
coats		
goat		
goal		
toe		

The double **oo** has three different sounds, the o̅o̅ as in **boot**, the o̯o as in **foot**, and the **ôo (r controlled)** as in **floor**. I teach it showing my foot - the o̯o in foot, put your boot on - the o̅o̅ in boot, and stomp your boot on the floor - the **ôo +r** in floor.

V̄V̄ (o̅o̅ as in moon)	words	patterns
noon		
food		
room		
VV (o̯o as in book)		
foot		
stood		
shook		
V̂V (ôo as in door)		
floor (vv + r)		
poor		

38

Fill in the blanks with your words.

goat foot food coats noon floor room stood shook poor

1. Did Sam get his _____ cleaned?

2. The big man cannot see his _____.

3. He _____ on the box.

4. Jack ate his _____ at _____.

5. Pick the _____ up off the _____.

6. The _____ _____ his foot.

7. The _____ girl needs a new coat.

Find your list words in the puzzle:

goat foot toe coats floor room stood shook poor

the (goat) poor here there some stood in box

room food toe noon screen floor shook people

either need have above five foot page shook

toe goal state ice coats miss glass time live soap

place goat poor whole goal states job map this

Lesson Twenty - VV (Vowel/Vowel Patterns) Continued

When two vowels go walking, the first one does the talking (says its name), and the second one is silent. The **long ā** vv pattern has two spellings. If the **long ā** sound is in the middle of the word, it is spelled with the **ai**. If the **long ā** comes at the end of the word, it is spelled with the **ay**.

v̄v	words	patterns
air (vv+r)*		
strain		
brain		
stairs (vv+r)*		
paint		
waist		
gray		
hay		
bay		
play		
2 Syllables always (v + l / v̄v + suffix)		
daily (v̄v / v̌)**		

*Remember, the letter 'r' has a strong sound, so when the 'r' comes after a vowel or two vowels, it affects the vowel sounds (controls it).

**For more on the v̌ pattern, see pages 82, 90, 92, or appendix page 20.*

Find the sentence in the puzzle.

Every day the man will strain his brain.

example:
It is his.

i	b	d	t
t	i	c	a
i	s	t	p
d	h	i	s

e	a	b	c	a	n	j	k	i	n	r	s	t
v	y	d	d	m	w	i	l	a	h	p	q	n
e	r	a	h	e	h	l	m	r	i	n	o	i
f	g	y	t	e	i	l	s	t	s	b	r	a

Fill in the blanks with your words.

air brain hay play gray

1. Did the man _____ with his dog?

2. The floor is _____ .

3. The goat likes _____ .

4. The man needs his _____ to live.

5. A brain needs _____ .

Lesson Twenty-one - VV (Vowel/Vowel Patterns)

VV ea - The 'ea' vowel combination has four different sounds. Lessons Twenty-one, Twenty-two, and Twenty-three will cover the different sounds the 'ea' combination makes.

VV ea - The ea vowel combination *ea as (ir) and ea as (er)*
Both of these ea combinations are affected by the strong 'r' sound.

vv ea (ir)	words	patterns
ear (vv+r)*		
hear (vv+r)*		
clear (vv+r)*		
year (vv+r)*		
dear (vv+r)*		
tear (vv+r)*		
spear (vv+r)*		
rear (vv+r)*		
near (vv+r)*		
vv ea (er) wear (vv+r)*		
bear (vv+r)*		
tear (vv+r)*		

For more on the v + r pattern, see page 56.

42

Find the sentence in the puzzle:

If you clear your ear, you will hear.

example:
It is his.

i	b	d	t
t	i	c	a
i	s	t	p
d	h	i	s

a	b	i	c	e	a	h	i	h	e	p
c	u	f	d	r	r,	y	j	l	a	r
l	o	y	e	u	f	o	k	l	l	o
e	a	r	y	o	g	u	w	i	m	n

Use your list words to fill in the blanks:

| spear | bear | near | wear | ear | tear | rear | year | clear | hear | tear | dear |

1. That man has a big _____ for hunting.

2. We just began a new school _____.

3. The space next to her is _____.

4. She went to the _____ of the plane.

5. The gray cat hurt his _____ in the woods.

6. Is it _____ us?

7. Did you _____ the _____ last night?

8. Please don't _____ your paper.

9. Jill had a _____ on her cheek.

10. Are you going to _____ pants there?

11. Kim wrote, "_____ Mom," at the top of her letter.

Lesson Twenty-two - VV (Vowel/Vowel Patterns)

VV ea - The 'ea' vowel combination has four different sounds. Lessons Twenty-one, Twenty-two, and Twenty-three will cover the different sounds the 'ea' combination makes.

̆vv ea (ĕ)

	words	patterns
read		
head		
meant		
lead		
death		
deaf		
breath		
bread		
sweat		
threads		
2 Syllables ready (v̆v/v́)*		
instead (v̆c/v̆v)		
weather (v̆v/v +r)**		

For more on the v́ pattern, see pages 82, 90, 92, or appendix page 20.

**For more on the v + r pattern, see page 56.*

Find this sentence in the puzzle:

I meant hot weather instead.

example:
It is on that.

i	c	d	t
t	b	e	a
i	s	c	h
a	o	n	t

n	o	i	p	t	r	s
a	e	m	b	c	i	j
t	w	e	a	d	h	k
h	t	o	n	e	g	l
e	a	h	t	f	a	d
r	i	n	s	t	e	m

Fill in the blanks with your list words:

instead   sweat   deaf   bread   weather   whether

1. She has not found out _____ she can go with you yet.

2. The class learned about _____ today.

3. Rick was covered with _____ after playing football all

   day.

4. I read about a _____ girl in class.

5. June used a lime _____ of a lemon.

6. The goat eats _____ all the time.

Lesson Twenty-three - VV (Vowel/Vowel Patterns)

VV ea - The 'ea' vowel combination has four different sounds. Lessons Twenty-one, Twenty-two, and Twenty-three will cover the different sounds the 'ea' combination makes.

	words	patterns
vv ea (ŭr)		
earth (vv+r)*		
heard (vv+r)*		
learn (vv+r)*		
2 Syllables early (vv+r/v́)*		
vv au (ô)		
fault		
pause		
2 Syllables because (v́/vv)**		
vv au (ă)		
aunt***		

*Remember, the letter 'r' has a strong sound, so when the 'r' comes after a vowel or two vowels, it affects the vowel sounds (controls it).

**For more on the v́ pattern, see pages 82, 90, 92, or appendix page 20.

***The au in aunt varies its sound from the short ă to ä. (The pronunciation changes, depending on which part of the country you live in.)

example: Did it see them?

His am at (Did) sat spot cat
up them has see me in (it)
that (see) into add just lot
from this (them) on him in (?)

Find the sentence in the puzzle.

My aunt heard that I will learn about the earth early next year.

In wear My tear learn of aunt class fault heard pause meant hot cake that

that Paul and I came to the nice off of sweat goat frog will happy know

learn wear lamb instead about near bears man walk the read have not

next lived front sad earth early run him than with plants next priest last

because pause pound both third year heard aunt turn stairs sure thread .

Find your list words in the puzzle:

aunt	because	pause	fault	early	heard	learn	earth

d	e	f	b	p	y	u	b	e
a	u	n	t	a	z	n	e	a
j	e	f	a	u	l	t	c	n
t	a	a	r	s	a	e	a	t
l	r	m	l	e	a	a	u	a
n	t	o	e	g	b	r	s	z
p	h	e	a	r	d	l	e	y
r	h	e	r	r	d	y	n	x
s	t	u	n	e	c	r	o	w

Lesson Twenty-four - VV Pattern Continued

The **VV ou** combination has seven different sounds. They will be grouped according to their sounds in Lessons Twenty-four and Twenty-five.

VV ou

vv ou (ou)
as in how

words	patterns

our

round

house*

ground

sound

found

scout

pound

cloud

2 Syllables
about (v́/vv)*

without (v̆c/vv)

outside (vv/v̄cæ)

* Sometimes words that end with an 's' sound will have a silent e after the 's'. (house, mouse, else, because)

For more on the v́ pattern, see pages 82, 90, 92, or appendix page 20.

Find your list words in the word search.

our	round	house	ground	sound	found
scout	pound	cloud	about	without	outside

a	h	p	s	r	s	s	o	b	h	g	r
b	i	w	i	t	o	h	u	t	o	h	s
c	j	o	f	s	u	w	r	o	u	n	d
d	g	r	o	u	n	d	z	a	s	i	t
e	k	n	u	t	d	x	s	b	e	j	u
p	o	u	n	d	y	a	c	o	f	k	v
f	l	m	d	u	c	l	o	u	d	l	d
o	u	t	s	i	d	e	u	t	e	m	p
g	w	i	t	h	o	u	t	c	d	n	o

Fill in the blanks with words from your list:

ground	found	scout	cloud	without	house	outside	round

1. Our tent is on the _____.

2. We cook pizza on a _____ pan.

3. The _____ _____ the bread at noon.

4. The sky was _____ a _____ in it.

5. He washed the _____ of the _____ with soap.

The **VV ou** combination has seven different sounds. They will be grouped according to their sounds in Lessons Twenty-four and Twenty-five.

VV ou

	words	patterns

vv ou (o͝o) as in book

would

could

should

vv ou (ô) as in aw
thought

vv ou as long ō (ō)
though

2 Syllables
although (v+l/vv)

vv ou as short ŭ (ŭ)
2 Syllables
country (vv/v́)*

vv ou as or (ôr)
your (vv + r)*

four (vv + r)*

course (vv + r)*

vv ou as moon(o͞o)
you

For more on the v́ pattern, see pages 82, 90, 92, or appendix page 20.

Find this sentence in the puzzle:

It's your four year course.

f	r	a	i	c	f	g
o	u	b	't	d	u	r
u	o	y	s	c	o	s
r	y	e	a	r	e	e

example: It is on that.

i	c	d	t
t	b	e	a
i	s	c	h
a	o	n	t

Find your words in the word search.

would could should thought though
although country your four course

a	l	t	h	o	u	g	h	m	p	u	z	s	d
b	t	h	o	u	g	h	l	n	q	v	a	h	e
c	c	o	u	n	t	r	y	o	r	q	f	o	f
c	o	u	l	d	j	f	o	u	r	y	o	u	r
d	o	g	c	o	u	r	s	e	s	o	b	l	p
e	s	h	o	r	t	i	k	w	o	u	l	d	h
f	h	t	h	o	u	g	h	t	t	y	c	j	f

Lesson Twenty-six - VV Pattern Continued

In the **VV** oi and oy pattern, the two vowels come together to make a new sound. Just like the ai and ay, the **ơi** is used when the vv pattern comes in the *middle* of the word. The **ơy** is used when the vv pattern is at the *end* of the word.

	VV ơi and ơy	
vv oi (ơi) in join	words	patterns
join		
voice* ℮ c=s		
oil		
boil		
moist		
coin		
points		
choice* ℮ c=s		
joint		
vv oy (ơi) in boy boy		
toy		
joy		

*When the letters 'c' and 'g' are followed by an 'e, i, or y', they go 'soft'. The 'c' gives the 's' sound and the 'g' gives the 'j' sound. For more on this, see page 94.

Find this sentence in the puzzle:

Don't boil the oil.

example:
It is on that.

i	c	d	t
t	b	e	a
i	s	c	h
a	o	n	t

d	a	b	c	e	o	e
o	b	o	d	h	i	l
n	't	i	l	t	f	g

Fill in the blanks with words from your list:

> boy choice join toy oil coin
> joy voice boil moist points joint

1. Fill the car with _____.

2. He is a big _____ who has to make a _____.

3. To fix the shelf, he must _____ the wood together at the

   corner _____.

4. My team got extra _____ for bringing the gold

   _____.

5. The man spoke with a big _____.

6. Dick must _____ the water in a pan.

7. The air is _____ after it has rained.

8. It is a _____ to play with a big _____.

VV ie as long ē, and ie as long ī

VV ie

The 'ie' has two sounds, either **long ē**, or **long ī**. The **ie** has the **long ē** sound when it is in the *middle* of a word. The **ie** has the **long ī** sound when it is at the *end* of a word. It remains the **long ī** sound when the **suffix 'd'** is added.

	words	patterns
vv ie as long ē (ē)		
priest		
fierce* (vv+r) (e makes 'c' go soft)**		
piece* (e makes 'c' go soft)		
ie as long ī (ī)		
pie		
tie		
tied*** (vv + suffix)		
died*** (vv + suffix)		

*Remember, the letter 'r' has a strong sound, so when the 'r' comes after a vowel or two vowels, it affects the vowel sounds (controls it).

**When the letters 'c' and 'g' are followed by an 'e, i, or y', they go 'soft'. The 'c' gives the 's' sound and the 'g' gives the 'j' sound. For more on this, see page 94.

***The 'ed' suffix has three different sounds. Sometimes it will give the 'd' sound (mailed); sometimes it will give the 't' sound (asked); and sometimes it will give the 'ed' sound (hunted).

Find this sentence in the puzzle:

example:
  It is on that.

i	c	d	t
t	b	e	a
i	s	c	h
a	o	n	t

The priest has a fierce piece of pie.

a	s	a	a	b	c
h	t	f	i	d	e
t	h	f	e	g	h
s	e	i	r	e	c
e	p	j	c	i	e
i	r	k	e	p	o
m	l	e	i	p	f

Find your list words in the puzzle:

priest	fierce	piece	pie	tie	tied	died

a	f	f	j	m	s	d
b	i	g	d	m	t	p
c	e	h	i	o	u	i
p	r	i	e	s	t	e
d	c	i	d	p	i	c
t	e	i	c	e	e	e
e	i	e	k	l	d	a
p	i	e	l	r	v	r

Lesson Twenty-eight - V + R Pattern

The letter 'r' is very strong; it is strong because it makes a growling sound. That strong sound scares the vowels so they can't give either their names (long sounds) or their nicknames (short sounds). Instead, the 'r' takes over, controlling the vowel. We call this an "r - controlled vowel" or a vowel + an r.

v + r (är)	words	patterns
are		
part		
large ⓔ g=j		
far		
hard		
car		
start		
dark		
warm		
care (v+rₑ)		
2 Syllables carry (v+r/v′)*		
3 Syllables area (v+r/v′/v′)*		

For more on the √ pattern, see pages 82, 90, 92, or appendix page 20.

Find your list words in the puzzle.

> are part large far hard car
> start dark warm care carry area

(are) join pie care pie so the does someone large

state far close joy pie carry fire far hard scout

pound heard start our fault would part ground

car wear warm year care lead read part area

scout hard far fire carry pie dark have close far

large one thought does care are ground dear state

instead part would fault our start state heard near

area close dark joy pie carry fire year far read hard

Use your list words to fill in the blanks:

> are part large far hard car
> start dark warm care carry area

That _____ of the park is the _____ where we parked

the _____. The _____ tree is in the center of it. It seems

_____ away but it's not. If we _____ walking now, it will

not be _____ when we get there. Do you _____ if I

_____ the _____ pie while we go there? Finally, we

_____ here at last! I'm glad it wasn't too _____ to get

here.

Lesson Twenty-nine - V + R Pattern

ir and ur

The letter 'r' is very strong; it is strong because it makes a growling sound. That strong sound scares the vowels so they can't give either their names (long sounds) or their nicknames (short sounds). Instead, the 'r' takes over, controlling the vowel. We call this an "r - controlled vowel" or a vowel + an r.

v + r
ir (ur)

first

girl

third

ur (ûr)
sure (v+re)

turn

turned (v + r , suffix)

2 Syllables
surface*
(v+r/v̄ce, ⓒ)
                c=s

Words	Patterns

*When the letters 'c' and 'g' are followed by an 'e, i, or y', they go 'soft'. The 'c' gives the 's' sound and the 'g' gives the 'j' sound. For more on this, see page 94.

Find your list words in the puzzle:

first girl sure third turn surface turned

priest join (first) are part third pound meant

sure tear aunt ham turn long sure earth back

stairs surface breath girl hay waist pain turned

stood floor dove third without surface both of

girl play bay here large first turned about turn

Complete the story using your list words. You may use them more than once.

first girl sure third turn surface turned

Mary was not _____ if she would be the _____ girl or the _____ girl in line. She hoped she was the first _____ be-cause she would get to take her _____ next. She _____ around and found that the _____ that she was to skate on was wet. Now Mary wants to be not even _____, but last!

Lesson Thirty - V + R Pattern

ôr and w + or

The letter 'r' is very strong; it is strong because it makes a growling sound. That strong sound scares the vowels so they can't give either their names (long sounds) or their nicknames (short sounds). Instead, the 'r' takes over, controlling the vowel. We call this an "r - controlled vowel" or a vowel + an r. The V + r (or) has two different sounds. It gives the (ôr) sound in 'for', unless there is a 'w' in front of it. If there is a 'w' in front of it, the 'or' gives the (ur) sound, ex.: world, work, worst.

v + r (ôr)

for

or

more

form

short

2 Syllables

story (v+r/v′)*

morning (v+r/v+ng)

order (v+r/v+r)

3 Syllables

important (v̆c/v+r/v̆c)

Words beginning with w + v + r

words

work

world

For more on the v′ pattern, see pages 82, 90, 92, or appendix page 20.
For more on the v + ng, see page 72.

Find your words in the word search:

| morning work story world order more |
| words short or form for important |

o	p	i	m	c	o	m	o	r	a	n	t	t
p	l	f	o	r	m	r	l	m	o	d	f	s
e	e	o	r	w	m	o	r	f	a	r	e	o
d	d	r	e	o	c	m	o	w	o	r	l	d
i	m	p	o	r	t	a	n	t	n	p	o	r
p	c	m	h	d	j	r	e	s	l	d	r	l
o	w	o	r	s	h	o	r	t	b	f	d	d
r	o	r	d	e	r	b	t	o	p	s	c	t
t	r	e	l	d	f	m	o	r	n	i	n	g
n	k	m	a	r	h	o	r	y	r	t	b	a

Fill in the blanks with words from your list:

| morning work story world order more |
| words short or form for important |

1. The _____ is round.

2. We _____ in the _____.

3. It is _____ to read the _____.

4. Do you want _____ of the food?

5. She put the books in _____.

6. Do you want to work _____ pie _____ cake?

7. Did you take the short _____ or the long form?

8. This _____ is too _____.

Lesson Thirty-one - V + R Pattern Continued

The letter 'r' is very strong; it is strong because it makes a growling sound. That strong sound scares the vowels so they can't give either their names (long sounds) or their nicknames (short sounds). Instead, the 'r' takes over, controlling the vowel. We call this an "r - controlled vowel" or a vowel + an r.

v + r 'er'

words	patterns

were (wŭr)

her (hūr)

there (ther)

where (hwer)

here (hir)

2 Syllables
other (ŭc/v+r)

after (ŭc/v+r)

very (v+ r/v́)*

water (v́/v+r)*

under (ŭc/v+r)

never (ŭc/v+r)

ever (ŭc/v+r)

mother (ŭc/v+r)

father (v́/v+r)

paper (v́/v+r)*

For more on the v́ pattern, see pages 82, 90, 92, or appendix page 20.

Find the sentence in the puzzle:

example: Did it see them?

His · am at (Did) sat spot cat
up them has see me in (it)
that (see) into add just lot
from this (them) on him in (?)

Mother and father never put the paper in the water.

were there short form Mother more to come some and

her one help which father list top seem her to never have

put oil coin be new soon did went our the hear life

pause paper come now here day clear in the sweat

ground were here that would water put and ready .

Fill in the blanks with your list words:

| ever her were where after there other here under paper |

1. Where is the _____ piece of _____?

2. Did you look over _____ _____ this stack of

   papers?

3. It is over _____.

4. I looked forever and _____.

5. _____ you coming with me to give it to _____?

6. _____ did Jack go _____ the game?

The letter 'r' is very strong; it is strong because it makes a growling sound. That strong sound scares the vowels so they can't give either their names (long sounds) or their nicknames (short sounds). Instead, the 'r' takes over, controlling the vowel. We call this an "r - controlled vowel" or a **vowel + an r**.

v + r 'er'	er - continued	
	words	patterns
2 Syllables better (v̆c/v+r)		
answer (v̆c/v+r)		
perhaps (v+r/v̆c)		
certain (v+r/vv)		
matter (v̆c/v+r)		
river (v̆c/v+r)		
whether (v̆c/v+r)		
either (v̄x/v+r)		
summer (v̆c/v+r)		
weather (v̆x/v+r)		
pattern (v̆c/v+r)		
center (v̆c/v+r)		

Fill in the blanks with your list words:

| whether summer center matter either weather |
| perhaps answer pattern better river |

1. The _____ in the _____ is

   _____ warm or hot.

2. _____ it won't _____ if Jason comes late.

3. The _____ flows through the _____ of town.

4. She wants to know _____ this _____

   is _____ than the other one.

5. Tom copied the _____ on his paper.

Find your list words in the puzzle:

| whether summer center matter either weather |
| perhaps answer pattern better river |

The letter 'r' is very strong; it is strong because it makes a growling sound. That strong sound scares the vowels so they can't give either their names (long sounds) or their nicknames (short sounds). Instead, the 'r' takes over, controlling the vowel. We call this an "r - controlled vowel" or a vowel + an r.

er - continued

v + r 'er'

	words	patterns
3 Syllables another (v̆c/v̆c/v+r)		
every (v̆c/v+r/v́)		
together (v́/v̆c/v+r)		
however (v+w/v̆c/v+r)*		
several (v̆c/v+r/v+l)**		
remember (v́/v̆c/v+r)		
understand (v̆c/v+r/v̆c)		
4 Syllables American (v́/v+r/v̆c/v̆c)***		

The v + w pattern is discussed on page 68.

The v * l pattern is discussed on page 76.

For more on the v́ pattern, see pages 82, 90, 92, or appendix page 20.

Find the sentence in the puzzle:

Together we remember the American winner.

example:
It is on that.

i	c	d	t
t	b	e	a
i	s	c	h
a	o	n	t

t	w	r	i	c	i
o	e	e	m	a	n
g	t	m	r	n	c
e	e	a	i	w	r
t	h	r	a	i	e
h	t	e	b	n	n
e	r	e	b	m	e
r	w	e	r	e	m

Fill in the blanks with words from your list:

| American every another several however |
| remember together understand |

1. We can play tag _____ day.

2. _____ of us went outside.

3. _____, Sara will _____ his speech.

4. It is wet _____ day it rains.

5. The five year old can _____ where she lives.

6. We are all going _____.

7. They will bring an _____ flag to the parade.

Lesson Thirty-four - V + W Pattern

Like the letter 'r', the letter 'w' is also a strong, controlling sound. The vowels sometimes use their long sound when they are followed by a 'w' (snow). Other times the 'w'
slightly changes the vowel sound - controlls it (how).

v + w

words	patterns

v + w [aw] (ô)
saw

draw

v + w [ew] (o͞o)

new

few

knew

v + w [ow] (o͡u)
as in cow
how

now

down

town

3 Syllables
however (v+w/v̆c/v+r)

68

Find your list words in the puzzle:

new	town	saw	however	how
draw	few	now	knew	down

down	up	near	far	high	meat	saw
above	wet	bug	feel	felt	few	fair
here	there	however	wear	our	ready
new	head	our	bread	knew	gate	bear
take	town	now	brown	cow	pause of
five	space	face	fire	draw	house	how

Fill in the blanks with words from your list:

new town saw however how draw few now knew down

1. Jill _____ how to spell all of the words.

2. If you want to go to Old _____, turn to the left.

3. Did you _____ a _____ picture?

4. Jan _____ the ants in the garden.

5. There is a saying, "_____ _____ brown cow."

6. Jack lives _____ the street from Sam.

7. _____, I knew only a _____ people at the party.

Lesson Thirty-five - V +W Pattern

Like the letter 'r', the letter 'w' is also a strong, controlling sound. The vowels sometimes use their long sound when they are followed by a 'w' (snow). Other times the 'w'
slightly changes the vowel sound - controlls it (how).

v + w (ow) long ō (ō)	v + w words	patterns
know		
own		
show		
grow		
shown		
snow *2 Syllables* below (v́/v+w)*		

For more on the v́ pattern, see pages 82, 90, 92, or appendix page 20.

Find your words in the word search:

know	own	show	grow	shown	snow	below

s	b	e	l	o	w
n	s	w	k	w	k
s	h	o	w	n	n
n	o	o	w	h	o
o	w	g	r	o	w
w	h	e	b	l	o

Fill in the blanks with words from your list:

own	shown	snow	know	grow	show	below

1. However, the _____ is _____ the window.

2. Rick has _____ us the way to town.

3. Did you _____ how he did it?

4. Now is the time to _____ what you _____ .

5. She saw how to _____ the plants.

The **'ng'** gives a twang sound to the vowels. The vowels seem to slightly change their sounds because of the twang.

v + ng (ing)	words	patterns
thing		
2 Syllables something (sight/v+ng)		
being (v́/v+ng)*		
during (v+r/v+ng)		
morning (v+r/v+ng)		
living (v̆c/v+ng)		
nothing (v̆c/v+ng)		
3 Syllables anything (v̆c/v́/v+ng)*		

For more on the v́ pattern, see pages 82, 90, 92, or appendix page 20.

Find your list words in the puzzle:

| being living nothing thing morning something anything during |

a	n	y	i	n	g	m	d	t	h
n	g	s	o	m	e	t	u	n	l
b	e	g	i	g	n	o	r	p	i
d	m	u	b	r	n	g	i	i	v
s	o	m	e	t	h	i	n	g	i
m	r	o	i	r	n	t	g	i	n
l	n	g	n	o	t	h	i	n	g
l	i	v	g	y	n	i	n	g	d
a	n	y	t	h	i	n	g	s	o
n	g	h	i	g	t	g	n	y	a

Fill in the blanks with your list words:

| being living nothing thing morning something anything during |

1. _____ is better than _____.

2. _____ can happen _____ the

   _____.

3. The piece of pie is _____ cut now.

4. The tree frog is _____ in the forest.

5. The main _____ is to call home.

Lesson Thirty-seven - V + NG and V + NK Pattern

The **'ng'** gives a twang sound to the vowels. The vowels seem to slightly change their sounds because of the twang.

	words	patterns
v + ng (ong)		
long		
2 Syllables		
along (v′/v+ng)		
among (v′/v+ng)		
v + ng (ang)		
change (v+ng & g=j)		
2 Syllables		
language (v+ng/vv & g=j)		
v + ng (eng)		
2 Syllables		
English (v+ng/v̆c)		
v + ng (oung)		
young (vv+ng)		
v + nk (ink)		
think (v+nk)		

74

Find your list words in the puzzle:

long along among change language English young think

e	t	h	i	n	k	a	l
n	h	t	i	o	c	p	o
g	l	o	n	e	h	y	n
l	a	n	g	u	a	g	e
i	e	l	g	l	n	a	g
s	y	o	u	n	g	l	l
h	c	n	l	n	e	o	a
e	n	g	o	s	h	n	n
a	m	o	n	g	a	g	e

Use your list words in the sentences:

long along among change language English young think

1. We speak _____ in the United States.

2. Pete will _____ before he acts.

3. Is the rope _____ or short?

4. I found the dish _____ the pans.

5. Did you come _____ with her?

6. He will _____ his pants before playing.

7. It is easy for the _____ to learn the _____.

Lesson Thirty-Eight - V+ L Pattern

The 'l' sound is also strong. Sometimes the 'l' slightly changes the vowel sound (all and doll). Other times it *masks* the vowel sound by almost overpowering it (well, ill, and old).

v + l [al] (ôl)	words	patterns
all		
small		
half (v̆c, l is silent)		
walked (v+l, suffix)		
2 Syllables almost (v+l/sight)		
special (v̆c/ ① c=s v+l) *3 Syllables* several (v̆c/v+r/v+l)		
already (v+l/v̆x/v́)*		
finally (v́/v+l/v́)*		

For more on the v́ pattern, see pages 82, 90, 92, or appendix page 20.

Fill in the blanks of the story with your list words:

| all small half ball walked almost special several already finally |

It was to be a _____ day. The boys were _____

there. They _____ and came to the _____ room.

The floor was _____ covered with balloons. A large red

_____ was also on the floor. _____ of the boys sat

on the ball and _____ fell off. They _____ had a

good time. The day was _____ over.

Find your list words twice in the puzzle:

| all small half ball walked almost special several already finally |

joy   plants   add   all   yet   asked   (already)   something

gave   state   ball   fine   hay   strain   finally   air   fell   of

thing   special   anything   bake   best   never   walked   same   and

better   small   saw   town   ball   several   however   here   room   day

where   who   anything   half   show   small   down   all   lead   head

several   breath   close   almost   space   here   fire   cake   morning

anything   never   half   walked   same   and   better   saw

hay   strain   almost   finally   air   now   fell   of   thing   special   joy

plants   add   yet   fall   asked   like   already   something   gave

77

Lesson Thirty-Nine - V + L Pattern Continued

The 'l' sound is also strong. Sometimes the 'l' slightly changes the vowel sound (all and doll). Other times it *masks* the vowel sound by almost overpowering it (well, ill, and old)

v + l (el)

words   patterns

well

felt

held

else*

2 Syllables
themselves (v̆c/v+l & suffix)

itself (v̆c/v+l)

v + l (il)
will

still

wild

t	w	i	l	e	a	p	p	e
e	w	h	a	t	a	w	d	n
s	h	s	e	e	t	e	l	t
e	a	p	?	l	s	l	i	h
s	v	h	l	s	l	l	w	n
h	m	a	l	e	h	?	e	e
f	t	p	i	w	t	e	h	p
l	s	p	e	n	t	o	t	w

* Sometimes words that end with an 's' sound will have a silent e after the 's'. (house, mouse, else, because)

Fill in the blanks with your list words:

| well felt hold else will still wild themselves itself |

1. The goats ate by _____.

2. There is _____ a lot of time left.

3. The plant will _____ _____ up.

4. He _____ the _____ animal.

5. _____ someone _____ please help?

6. Tom is not sick; he is _____.

Find the sentence:

example:

It is on that.

i	c	d	t
t	b	e	a
i	s	c	h
a	o	n	t

What else will happen to the wild well?

t	w	i	l	e	a	p	p	e
e	w	h	a	t	a	w	d	n
s	h	s	e	e	t	e	l	t
e	a	p	?	l	s	l	i	h
s	v	h	l	s	l	l	w	n
h	m	a	l	e	h	?	e	e
f	t	p	i	w	t	e	h	p
l	s	p	e	n	t	o	t	w

Lesson Forty - V+L Pattern Continued
v + l and c + le

The **'l'** sound is also strong. Sometimes the **'l'** slightly changes the vowel sound (all and doll). Other times it *masks* the vowel sound by almost overpowering it (well, ill, and old).

v + l (ol)

words	patterns
old | | |
cold | | |
hold | | |

c + le

As in the last set, the **'l'** is a strong letter. When you have an **'le'** at the end of a *two* - or *three-syllable word*, it grabs the consonant in front of it to form the syllable.

c + le

words	patterns
2 Syllables people (v̄x/c+le) | | |
simple (v̆c/c+le) | | |
3 Syllables example (v̆c/v̆c/c+le) | | |
possible (v̆c/v́/c+le) | | |

Fill in the blanks with your list words:

| old cold hold people simple example possible |

1. It is _____ for the _____ man to walk with a

cane.

2. Bob never gets _____; he is always warm.

3. Mom will show you an _____.

4. Pat thinks it is _____ to bake a cake.

5. Many _____ will _____ this book.

Find your list words in the puzzle:

| old cold hold people simple example possible |

l	e	x	a	m	e	o	p	p
c	o	p	c	o	l	d	o	e
m	p	d	o	l	d	e	s	o
i	e	i	l	p	e	o	s	l
h	o	l	d	e	x	a	i	p
s	p	b	e	s	s	i	b	l
a	l	l	s	i	m	p	l	e
x	e	x	a	m	p	l	e	s
s	i	m	m	p	l	e	l	d

81

Lesson Forty-one - V′ Pattern
V′ Pattern

The vowel sound is very strong here. It usually says its name because there is no consonant right next to it, protecting it. This is an **open syllable.** *When a syllable ends with a vowel sound, it must give a strong sound. The vowel usually gives its long sound when it is at the end of a syllable.* If the vowel is a **'y'**, then it gives the **long ī** sound if it is at the end of a one syllable word **(my)**. When the **'y'** is at the end of a two-syllable word, it gives the **long ē** sound **(funny)**.

There are *two instances* when you have this **v′** pattern. The first is when you have a vowel at the end of a one syllable word **(me)**.

v′	words	patterns
be		
he		
I		
we		
she		
so		
no		
go		
my		
me		
why		
try		
sky		

Fill in the blanks with your list words:

he	try	my	why	sky	go	I	be	she	so	no	we

1. _____ dog is big.

2. _____ is big and _____ is little.

3. Did the car _____ fast?

4. Rick will _____ to write his paper now.

5. _____ is it in a box and not in a bag?

6. The cloud is up in the _____.

7. _____ want to eat the pie now.

8. Nick will leave now, _____ he will not be late.

9. _____, I can go after all.

10. Mike will _____ here very soon.

11. _____ are not sure who is first and who is third.

Find this sentence in the puzzle:

example: Did it see them?

His	am	at	(Did)	sat	spot	cat
up	them	has	see	me	in	(it)
that	(see)	into	add	just	lot	
from	this	(them)	on	him	in	(?)

Why did the fly try to go up in the sky?

bear	Why	up	the	did	hear	there	turn
early	the	who	sleep	fly	in	try	at	pot
to	on	go	table	up	did	in	why	ice
first	the	third	sky	sure	ran	six	I	we	?

Lesson Forty-two - V́ Pattern
V́ Pattern

The vowel sound is very strong here. It usually says its name because there is no consonant right next to it, protecting it. This is an **open syllable.** *When a syllable ends with a vowel sound, it must give a strong sound. The vowel usually gives its long sound when it is at the end of a syllable.*

Lessons Forty-two through Forty-six have words from the second instance. This is when you have an open vowel - a vowel at the end of a syllable in a multi-syllable word (ṓ/ver, á/long, á/gṓ).The vowel is not closed off or protected by a consonant. In the word *pic/nic,* the *'c'* closes the syllable each time, so the *'i'* can give its short sound.

In a 2 or 3-syllable word, the *v́ (open syllable) may be in any or all of the syllables (i/de/a).

v́ in the first syllable of the word

	words	patterns
around (v́/vv)		
along (v́/v+ng)		
ago (v́/v́)		
alone (v́/v̄ce)		
again (v́/v̄x)		
away (v́/v̄x)		
enough (v́/vv)		
even (v́/v̌c)		
between (v́/v̄x)		

Find the sentence in the puzzle:

Don't go away alone.

c	a	y	a	a
d	w	d	l	b
e	a	o	o	f
h	o	n	n	e
i	g	't	j	g
k	l	m	n	o

example:

It is on that.

i	c	d	t
t	b	e	a
i	s	c	h
a	o	n	t

Find your list words in the puzzle:

around along ago alone again away enough even between

a	c	e	l	a	l	o	n	g	n
b	d	h	k	r	i	j	k	l	m
f	g	i	j	o	a	l	o	n	e
m	e	n	o	u	g	h	h	g	v
a	g	a	i	n	o	d	e	f	e
n	o	w	e	d	w	x	b	c	n
q	p	a	b	e	t	w	e	e	n
r	s	y	t	t	u	v	y	z	a

Lesson Forty-three - V́ Pattern Continued

The vowel sound is very strong here. It usually says its name because there is no consonant right next to it, protecting it. This is an **open syllable.** *When a syllable ends with a vowel sound, it must give a strong sound. The vowel usually gives its long sound when it is at the end of a syllable.*

Lessons Forty-two through Forty-six have words from the second instance. This is when you have an open vowel - a vowel at the end of a syllable in a multi-syllable word (ō´/ver, a´/long, a´/go´).The vowel is not closed off or protected by a consonant. In the word *pic/nic,* the *'c'* closes the syllable each time, so the *'i'* can give its short sound.

In a 2 or 3-syllable word, the *v´ (open syllable) may be in any or all of the syllables (i/de/a).

v´ in the first syllable of the word

	words	patterns
became (v´/v̄cℯ)		
below (v´/v+w)		
become (v´/v̄cℯ)		
being (v´/v+ng)		
behind (v´/sight)		
begin (v´/v̆c)		
because* (v´/vv)		
began (v´/v̆c)		
before (v´/v̄cℯ)		

* Sometimes words that end with an 's' sound will have a silent e after the 's'. (house, mouse, else, because)

86

Find the sentence in the puzzle:

He began behind the box.

example:

It is on that.

i	c	d	t
t	b	e	a
i	s	c	h
a	o	n	t

h	e	b	o	x
t	h	e	b	e
d	a	n	a	g
n	e	b	b	c
i	h	d	e	f

Find your list words in the puzzle:

became	below	become	being	behind	begin	because	began	before

b	e	f	o	r	e	s	b	m	l
b	e	f	d	g	b	h	e	j	k
e	v	w	c	b	a	a	i	y	x
c	s	r	q	p	c	o	n	m	l
a	d	e	f	c	e	b	g	i	h
u	n	o	g	e	b	e	l	o	w
s	v	w	a	b	e	g	i	n	v
e	p	s	b	e	c	a	m	e	m
g	h	k	l	t	o	n	i	f	e
w	w	y	d	e	m	c	b	a	z
n	a	g	i	b	e	h	i	n	d
j	p	v	u	e	e	t	s	r	t

Lesson Forty-four - V´ Pattern Continued

The vowel sound is very strong here. It usually says its name because there is no consonant right next to it, protecting it. This is an **open syllable.** *When a syllable ends with a vowel sound, it must give a strong sound. The vowel usually gives its long sound when it is at the end of a syllable.* If the vowel is a **'y'**, then it gives the **long ī** sound if it is at the end of a one syllable word **(my).** When the **'y'** is at the end of a two-syllable word, it gives the **long ē** sound **(funny).**

Lessons Forty-two through Forty-six have words from the second instance. This is when you have an open vowel - a vowel at the end of a syllable in a multi-syllable word **(ō´/ver, a´/long, a´/go´).** The vowel is not closed off or protected by a consonant. In the word *pic/nic,* the *'c'* closes the syllable each time, so the *'i'* can give its short sound.

In a 2 or 3-syllable word, the *v´ (open syllable) may be in any or all of the syllables (i/de/a).

*v´

	words	patterns
tiny (v´/v̆)		
united (v´/v̄c(ℯ)/v̆c) _(the e has two jobs here - base word is unite)		
able (v´/c+le)		
table (v´/c+le)		
notice (v´/v̆c, ℯ_{c=s})		
over (v´/v+r)		
open (v´/v̆c)		
paper (v´/v+r)		

88

Find the sentence in the puzzle:

example: Did it see them?

His   am   at (Did) sat spot cat

up   them has see me in (it)

that (see) into add just lot

from this (them) on him in (?)

Is he able to open the paper?

here Is able he upon dear able for the

take to tied priest often fish these next

coin ball open choice second enough even

turn first the work story very short car

piece surface wind less then paper

top sun hand we she oil pie field ?

Fill in the blanks with your list words:

tiny united able table notice over open paper

Hint: If the word is used as a proper name, don't forget to capitalize it!

1. The _____ was on the _____.

2. _____ the _____ so you can read the directions.

3. The _____ States is a large country.

4. The green frog jumped _____ the snake.

5. The _____ butterfly was _____ to fly out of the

open window.

89

Lesson Forty-five - V́ Pattern Continued

The vowel sound is very strong here. It usually says its name because there is no consonant right next to it, protecting it. This is an **open syllable.** *When a syllable ends with a vowel sound, it must give a strong sound. The vowel usually gives its long sound when it is at the end of a syllable.* If the vowel is a **'y'**, then it gives the long ī sound if it is at the end of a one syllable word **(my)**. When the **'y'** is at the end of a two-syllable word, it gives the long ē sound **(funny)**.

Lessons Forty-two through Forty-six have words from the second instance. This is when you have an open vowel - a vowel at the end of a syllable in a multi-syllable word (ō´/ver, a´/long, a´/gō´). The vowel is not closed off or protected by a consonant. In the word *pic/nic,* the *'c'* closes the syllable each time, so the *'i'* can give its short sound.

In a 2 or 3-syllable word, the *v´ (open syllable) may be in any or all of the syllables (i/de/a).

v́

	words	patterns
3 Syllables		
every (v̆c/v+r/v́)		
usually (v̄c(ɛ)/v́/v+l/v́) (the e was dropped from the base word use when the suffix was added)		
family (v̆c/v̆c/v́)		
idea (v́/v́/v́)		
v́ (o) gives the o͞o sound		
to		
two		
who		
do		
2 Syllables into v̆c/v́)		

90

Find the sentence in the puzzle:

Who do you like?

example:

It is on that.

i	c	d	t
t	b	e	a
i	s	c	h
a	o	n	t

o	h	c	e	g
d	w	d	f	e
o	y	o	i	k
a	b	u	l	h

Fill in the blanks with your list words:

to two who do into every usually family idea

1. _____ is he?

2. _____ you go to class yet?

3. Is your _____ big or small?

4. Six and _____ are eight.

5. I go to school _____ day.

6. Pam _____ eats soup for lunch.

7. My mom has a great _____.

8. What do you want _____ do today?

9. My aunt placed the food _____ the bag before she went home.

Lesson Forty-six - V´ Pattern Continued

The vowel sound is very strong here. It usually says its name because there is no consonant right next to it, protecting it. This is an **open syllable.** *When a syllable ends with a vowel sound, it must give a strong sound. The vowel usually gives its long sound when it is at the end of a syllable.* If the vowel is a 'y', then it gives the long ī sound if it is at the end of a one syllable word **(my)**. When the 'y' is at the end of a two-syllable word, it gives the long ē sound **(funny).**

Lessons Forty-two through Forty-six have words from the second instance. This is when you have an open vowel - a vowel at the end of a syllable in a multi-syllable word (ō´/ver, a´/long, a´/go´). The vowel is not closed off or protected by a consonant. In the word *pic/nic,* the *'c'* closes the syllable each time, so the *'i'* can give its short sound.

In a 2 or 3-syllable word, the *v´ (open syllable) may be in any or all of the syllables (i/de/a).

v´ in the last syllable of the word

	words	patterns
many (v̆c/v´)		
very (v+r/v´)		
body (v̆c/v´)		
also (v+l/v´)		
country (xv̆/v´)		
city (v̆c/v´)		
any (v̆c/v´)		
carry (v+r/v´)		
easy (v̄x/v´)		
early (vv/v´)		
really (v̄x/v´)		
only (v̄c/v´)		

Fill in the blanks with your list words:

many very body also country city any carry easy early really only

1. It is too _____ to go to the _____ .

2. He is _____ the _____ person that can do the job.

3. Do you need to bring _____ plants to the _____ ?

4. Jake _____ likes the color red.

5. Dan has _____ books to _____ home.

6. Mike was out _____ late .

7. It is _____ for the frog to jump far.

8. Dick's _____ hurt after the ten mile hike.

Find your list words in the puzzle:

many very body also country city any carry easy
early really only

priest sure go home (many) have not city ham

country are if at any easy each read both now

large body meant ham very waist about she

because girl really wet Mary floor only are

world pie from choose also or form more for

any blanks how new old early world story now

morning begin away open carry ago notice

Lesson Forty-seven - Special Letters
C and G

The letters **'c'** and **'g'** are borrowers. When the letters **'c'** and **'g'** are followed by the vowels **'e'**, **'i'**, or **'y'**, they usually go soft. That means the **'c'** will give the **'s'** sound **(city)** instead of the **'k'** sound **(cat)**. The **'g'** will give the **'j'** sound **(page)** instead of the **'g'** sound **(goat)**.

c followed by e, i, or y	words	patterns
place (v̄cæ, (c) followed by e)		
once (sight, (c) followed by e)		
since (v̆c, (c) followed by e)		
face (v̄cæ, (c) followed by e)		
space (v̄cæ, (c) followed by e)		
voice (vv, (c) followed by e)		
piece (xv̄, (c) followed by e)		
ice (v̄cæ, (c) followed by e)		

Find your list words in the puzzle:

| voice | ice | piece | space | face | since | place | once |

p	i	c	i	a	s	e	c
p	l	a	c	e	p	c	s
n	c	e	e	f	a	c	e
o	n	v	o	i	c	e	o
l	s	c	n	c	e	p	l
p	i	e	c	e	e	c	a
l	n	s	e	p	v	o	i
a	c	p	o	e	c	n	p
c	e	l	a	v	l	c	o
e	p	c	e	c	s	n	i

Fill in the blanks with your list words:

| voice | ice | piece | space | face | since | place | once |

1. The _____ of _____ was cold.

2. Rick heard the _____ from the _____ shuttle.

3. Many stories start with the words, "_____ upon a time."

4. The _____ she moved over to was empty.

5. Pat has been away _____ June.

6. The clown has paint all over his _____.

Lesson Forty-eight - Special Letters Continued

C and G

The letters **'c'** and **'g'** are borrowers. When the letters **'c'** and **'g'** are followed by the vowels **'e'**, **'i'**, or **'y'**, they usually go soft. That means the **'c'** will give the **'s'** sound **(city)** instead of the **'k'** sound **(cat)**. The **'g'** will give the **'j'** sound **(page)** instead of the **'g'** sound **(goat)**.

c followed by e, i, or y
(2 Syllables)

sentence (v̆c/v̆c, $\underset{c=s}{ⓔ}$)

city (v̆c $\underset{c=s}{ⓘ}$ /v́)

certain (v+r $\underset{c=s}{ⓔ}$ / v̄x)

special (v̆c $\underset{c=s}{ⓔ}$ / v + l)

notice (v́/v̆c, $\underset{c=s}{ⓔ}$)

surface (v+r/v̆c, $\underset{c=s}{ⓔ}$)

distance (v̆c/v̆c, $\underset{c=s}{ⓔ}$)

g followed by e, i, or y
page (v̄cₑ, $\underset{g=j}{ⓔ}$)

change (v + ng, $\underset{g=j}{ⓔ}$)

words	patterns

Find your list words in the puzzle:

sentence city certain special notice surface distance page change

g	c	n	d	e	c	o	t	y	s
n	s	c	i	n	h	e	t	n	i
a	p	a	s	p	a	g	e	h	a
s	e	n	t	e	n	c	e	e	s
h	c	o	a	n	g	i	n	g	e
c	i	t	n	o	e	t	i	c	e
s	a	i	c	i	a	y	c	e	r
g	l	c	e	r	t	a	i	n	t
p	a	e	s	u	r	f	a	c	e

Find your list words in the puzzle:

sentence city certain special notice surface distance page change

morning   do   you   (surface)   words   round   cake   use   gives

for   order   more   city   third   turn   special   page   food   books

choose   notice   words   story   form   fierce   piece   above

happy   dad   distance   done   someone   come   have   not

oh   how   page   very   country   change   wet   wants   around

sentence   them   list   living   nothing   third   turn   books   use

shown   draw   important   more   puzzle   certain   came   space

Lesson Forty-nine - Silent Letters

CK   KN   WR

Rule for 'ck':

When a word ends with the 'k' sound, if the vowel is short, the 'k' is spelled with a 'ck'. If the vowel is long, the word is spelled with a 'k' and silent *e*.

'ck' and 'k*e*'	words	patterns
rock (v̆c)		
check (v̆c)		
back (v̆c)		
take (v̄c*e*)		
like (v̄c*e*)		
make (v̄c*e*)		
kn, *the 'k' is silent*		
know (v + w)		
knew (v + w)		
wr, *the 'w' is silent*		
write (v̄c*e*)		
wrote (v̄c*e*)		

Fill in the blanks with your list words:

| check rock back like make take know knew write wrote |

1. Jay found a big red _____ on the hike.

2. Jon _____ his friend a letter.

3. Did you _____ the play you saw yesterday?

4. You need to _____ your bed and _____the

   trash out.

5. I _____ I had seen her before today.

6. Lisa, will you please _____ your thank you notes?

7. He _____ she was going to be here.

8. Dad, will you please _____ the _____ yard for it?

Find your list words in the puzzle:

| check rock back like make |
| take know knew write wrote |

pound	third	(back)	front	late	to	here
know	day	play	here	there	mine	may	make
row	rock	bid	now	when	here	wrote
happy	sad	other	of	knew	the	in	city
band	cloud	does	some	most	take	at
house	scout	side	those	like	fire	wide
size	check	state	ice	kite	write	miss

Lesson Fifty - More Silent Letters

V + silent GH	GH as F	PH as F	TION (suffix)

	words	patterns

v + silent gh

brought

right

might

light

high

though

gh as f

2 Syllables

enough [v̄/x̄vgh(f)]

ph as f

phone (v̄ce)

tion (suffix)

question (v̆c/tion)

Since the u always follows the q,
it is not part of the vowel pattern.

Find your list words in the puzzle:

brought

right

might

light

high

though

enough

phone

question

o	r	b	o	u	i	t	h	p	r
n	h	r	o	p	g	h	o	h	i
e	n	o	u	g	h	h	e	o	g
e	q	u	e	s	t	i	o	n	h
n	u	g	q	u	e	g	t	e	t
o	e	h	p	h	t	h	o	u	g
u	s	t	i	o	n	m	i	g	h

Use your list words to fill in the story:
Hint: You will use some words more than once.

| brought   right   might   light   high   though   enough   phone   question |

Fred _____ a _____ with him on his hike. He thought

he _____ need it in the cave. There was not _____ light for

him to see. Fred was afraid that the roof of the cave would not be _____

_____. He might hit his head.The_____ was bright in the

cave. Fred was surprised to see a _____ with a _____ mark

on the table next to it. It was as _____ he was supposed to lift up the

phone. He lifted it up to listen to it. He was sure it was the _____ thing

to do. He was surprised when he heard a man tell him he had just won a prize, but he

must hurry home to get it. Fred ran home and found all of his friends there. They

_____ a cake over for a surprise birthday party.

Making Spelling Sense™
Appendix

Welcome to *Making Spelling Sense*™
Appendix

Pass out copies of the practice / test sheet.
[Be sure to use the correct Lesson sheet;
the sheets are to be used for pretests.]

Procedure for doing the pretest:

1. Remind the students which vowel pattern you are working with.

2. Give each word, a sound at a time. The students write each sound down in the first column as you say the sound. Be sure to check their papers for the correct vowel sounds while they are working, since so many students confuse the i with the ĕ. Also remind students if the vowel is in the v̄cɇ pattern, the silent ɇ is making the vowel say its name.

3. After you have said the sounds of the whole word, they (the students) say the word and write it again, in the second column.

4. Students write the vowel pattern in the third column.

5. Have students fold their papers on the dotted line. Then, with the fourth column facing them, have them write their words as you say them back to them.

6. Have students unford their papers and check their words.

7. Be sure to do both a practice test and a final test, to be sure the students have retained the concept and spelling of the words.

Lessons 1 - 11	Use the vowels {ă, ĕ, ĭ, ŏ, ŭ}		the combination letters:
V̆C Pattern	and consonants {b, c, d, f, g, h, j, k, l, m, n, p, r, s, t, v, w, x, y or ch, sh, th, wh, & ck}		

Write each sound here:	Rewrite your word here:	Spelling Pattern:	Practice Test:
o f t e n	often	vc/vc	often
s e c o n d	second	vc/vc	second
h i m s e l f	himself	vc/vc	himself
u p o n	upon	vc/vc	
c a n n o t	cannot	vc/vc	cannot
h u n d r e d	hundred	vc/vc	hundred
c o m m o n	common	vc/vc	common
h a p p e n	happen	vc/vc	happen
b o t t o m	bottom	vc/vc	bottom
s e n t e n ce	sentence	vc/vc,	sentence
(remind them about when c is		c followed by e - goes soft	
followed by an 'e', it goes soft)			

sample pretest page for lesson 11

Lessons 1 - 11. Use the vowels {**ă, ĕ, ĭ, ŏ, ŭ**} (For lesson 11 ⓔ꜀₌ₛ) the combination letters:

V̆C Pattern and consonants {**b, c, d, f, g, h, j, k, l, m, n, p, r, s, t, v, w, x, y** or **ch, sh, th, wh, & ck**}

Write your sounds here:	Rewrite your word here:	Spelling Pattern:	Practice Test:

Fold here:

appendix 3

Lessons 12 - 15	Use the vowels {ā, ē, ī, ō, & ū with the silent *e*}		the combination letters:

VCE Pattern

and consonants {c, d, f, g, k, l, m, n, p, qu, r, s, t, v, w, z, or **th, wh, & wr**}

Write each sound here:	Rewrite your word here:	Spelling Pattern:	Practice Test:

Fold here:

Sight Words

Use the vowels {**a, e, i, o**}

and consonants {**b, c, d, f, h, k, l, m, n, s, t, v** and combination letters **th** & **wh**}

Write your sounds here:	Rewrite your word here:	Spelling Pattern:	Practice Test:

Fold here:

Lesson 18

VV Pattern

Use the vowels {**ee, ea, ei, eo, er, ple, ɛ, & y**}   the combination letters:

and the consonants {**b, c, d, k, l, m, n, p, r, s, t, v, w,**   or   **th**}

Write each sound here:	Rewrite your word here:	Spelling Pattern:	Practice Test:

Fold here:

Lessons 19 & 20 | Use the vowels {oa, oe, oo, ai, ay, al, & y} and the combination letters:

VV Pattern | and the letters: {b, c, d, f, g, h, k, l, m, n, p, r, s, t, w or ch, sh}

Write your sounds here: | Rewrite your word here: | Spelling Pattern: | Practice Test:

Fold here:

Lessons 21, 22, & 23	Use the vowels {**ea, y, i, er, au, e, and æ**} the combination letters:		
VV Pattern	{**b, c, d, f, h, l, m, n, p, r, s, t, w, y or th**}		
Write each sound here:	Rewrite your word here:	Spelling Pattern:	Practice Test:
		Fold here:	

Lessons 24 & 25

VV Pattern

Use the vowels {**ou, i, e, a, y & æ**}

Use the consonants {**b, c, d, f, g, h, l, n, p, r, s, t, w, y,** or **th, sh, gh**} the combination letters:

Write your sounds here:	Rewrite your word here:	Spelling Pattern:	Practice Test:

Fold here:

Lesson 26 & 27

VV Pattern

Use the vowels {oi, oy, & ie}

Use the consonants {b, c, d, f, j, l, m, n, p, r, s, t, v   or **ch**}

the combination letters:

Write each sound here:	Rewrite your word here:	Spelling Pattern:	Practice Test:
		Fold here:	

Lessons 28 - 33 — Use the vowels {ar, er, ir, or, ur, ă, ā, ĕ, ē, ɛ̌, ĭ, ŏ, ĕi, ĕa, āi ow, al, & y} (Lessons 28+29 ⓔ g=j, ⓔ c=s)

V + R Pattern — and the consonants {b, c, d, f, g, h, l, m, n, p, r, s, t, v, w, or **sh, th, & wh**}

Write your sounds here:	Rewrite your word here:	Spelling Pattern:	Practice Test:

Fold here:

Lessons 34 - 35   Use the vowels {aw, ew, ow, ĕ, er}   the combinations

V + W Pattern   and consonants {b, d, f, g, h, k, l, n, r, s, t, v, w   or   sh, & kn}

Write each sound here:	Rewrite your word here:	Spelling Pattern:	Practice Test:

Fold here:

V + ng & V + nk

Use the vowels {**ang, eng, ing, ink, ong, oung, a, i, o, ɛ, ua, & y**} (Lesson 37 ⓔ g=j)

or the consonants {**b, d, g, l, m, n, r, s, v, y**} or **ch, sh, & th**

Write your sounds here:	Rewrite your word here:	Spelling Pattern:	Practice Test:

Fold here:

appendix 13

Lessons 38 - 40 V + l and C + le Pattern	Use the vowels {al, el, ol, il, eo, e, er, ea, æ, i, o, y, ble, ple} (Lesson 38 ☉) or the consonants {c, d, f, h, k, l, m, n, p, r, s, t, v, w or th}

Write each sound here:	Rewrite your word here:	Spelling Pattern:	Practice Test:

Fold here:

Lessons 41 - 46 Use the vowels {aˊ, eˊ, iˊ, oˊ, uˊ, yˊ, ou, ai, ee, er, ea, a, au, ow, i, ing, ong, or, ble, ε, & yˊ}(Lessonˢ 44) **Vˊ Pattern** and the consonants **{b, c, d, f, g, h, k, l, m, n, p, r, s, t, v, w** or **ng, gh, sh, wh}**

Write your sounds here:	Rewrite your word here:	Spelling Pattern:	Practice Test:
		Fold here:	

appendix 15

Lessons 47 & 48 **Borrowers c and g**	Use the vowels {a, o, ie, æ, e, e, er, oi, i, o, ur, ai, al, ang, y}(Lesson 48 $\textcircled{æ}$ $\textcircled{i}$ $\textcircled{æ}$ c=s, c=s, g=j) and the consonants {c, d, f, g, l, n, p, r, s, t, v and the combination letters **ch**}

Write each sound here:	Rewrite your word here:	Spelling Pattern:	Practice Test:
		Fold here:	

appendix 16

Lessons 49 - 50   Use the vowels {**a, e, ɛ, ew, ow, ou, i, o, u**} and the consonants {**b, h, k, l, m, n, qu, r, s, t, w**}
Silent letters or combination letters **ch, ck, kn, wr, gh, gh as f, ph as f, th, tion(suffix)**}

Write your sounds here:	Rewrite your word here:	Spelling Pattern:	Practice Test:
		Fold here:	

Rules for Suffixes

Suffixes are a letter, syllable, or group of syllables that are added to a word to make it plural, change its meaning, or form a new word (change jump to jumps, jumping, or jumper).

Doubling final consonants:

If you are adding a suffix to a one syllable, one vowel and one consonant word, you **must double the final consonant before you add the suffix** (change **bat** to **batter**). The doubling of the consonant protects the vowel, so it can keep its short sound (change **set** to **setting**).

sit	sitter	jog	jogging
wag	wagging	hop	hopping
kid	kidding	bet	better

What do you do when your base or root word ends with a vowel?

If the suffix you are adding begins with a vowel (***ing, ed, er,*** or ***est***), **drop the magic or evil e**. The vowel from the suffix will take over. Then add the suffix. If the suffix you are adding begins with a consonant (*s*), **just add the *s***

take	takes	rule	ruler
use	used	page	pages
be	being	go	going
smile	smiling	wave	waving

Comparing the first two rules: short vowel words and long vowel words with suffixes:

You need to double the final consonant in a short vowel word in order to protect the vowel, keep it short (change **hop** to **hopping**). If the vowel is long, if the word ends with a silent *e*, drop it, and add the suffix, (change **hope** to **hoping**). If the word is a v´ pattern, just add the suffix, (**change go** to **going**).

late	later	hot	hotter
stop	stopping	rope	roped
cute	cutest	cut	cutting
hit	hitter	skate	skating

Should you add an *s* or an *es*?

If the word has one syllable when you say the plural, you just add an *'s'* (change **girl** to **girls**). If the word has two syllables when you say the plural, add *'es'* (change **fix** to **fixes**).

boy	boys		dish	dishes
week	weeks		lunch	lunches
help	helps		glass	glasses

Adding *ing:*

Just add the *'ing'* to the base or root word (change **wait** to **waiting**).

jump	jumping		sting	stinging
fly	flying		see	seeing
park	parking		camp	camping

Adding *ed:*

The *'ed'* suffix has three different sounds. Sometimes it will give the *'d'* sound (**mailed**); sometimes it will give the *'t'* sound (**mixed**); and sometimes it will give the *'ed'* sound (**hunted**). You need to become familiar with all three sounds for the *'ed'* suffix.

sail	sailed		seem	seemed
fix	fixed		spank	spanked
paint	painted		start	started

Adding *er* and *est:*

Just add the *'er'* or *'est'* to the base or root word (change **fight** to **fighter** and **smooth** to **smoothest**).

short	shorter	shortest	bright	brighter	brightest
smooth	smoother	smoothest	hard	harder	hardest
small	smaller	smallest	clean	cleaner	cleanest
loud	louder	loudest	nice	nicer	nicest

What do I do with words that end in a *y?*

If your word ends with a *'y'*, change the *'y'* to *'i'* and then add your suffix (change **penny** to **pennies**).

pony	ponies	baby	babies
lady	ladies	daddy	daddies
party	parties	hobby	hobbies
fry	fried	study	studied
copy	copier	dry	drier

Other common suffixes:
tion, ment, ly, er, ful

action	addition	wonderful	friendly
nation	compliment	swiftly	quiter
agreement	quickly	slowly	starter

Open and Closed Syllables

A closed syllable is a syllable that ends with a consonant. The consonant protects the vowel, so the vowel can say its nickname. An open syllable is a syllable that ends with a vowel. The vowel must be strong here, so it usually says its name. When you have a two syllable word, sometimes the first syllable is an open syllable (v ;) (**o pen** or **ta ble**) and sometimes its closed (**sim ple** or **hap pen**). When spelling multi-syllable words, spell them a syllable at a time. If the vowel in the syllable is long, leave the syllable open and go on to spell the next syllable. If the vowel is short, close the syllable with a consonant (which protects the vowel so it can use its short sound), and then go on to the next syllable. *Even though vowels that are controlled by r's or w's, are not short or long, the consonants 'r' and 'w' make the syllable act as a closed one.*

Open	Closed	Open	Closed
ta ble	can dy	e ven	sud den
cra zy	ug ly	sta ple	cir cle
a ble	sev en	ba by	pur ple
pa per	mis ter	la ter	riv er
fi nal	den tist	la dy	aw ful
fa vor	doc tor	fro zen	mem ber
e lect	up per	ze bra	muf fin

Prefixes

Prefixes are short syllables added to the beginning of words. The prefix changes the meaning of the base word. The prefixes *'un'* and *'re'* reverse the action of the base word (**return** or **unlock**).

Common prefixes are:
re, un, ex, de, con, com, dis, mis, non, and *pre.*

un + real	unreal	un + load	unload
un + lucky	unlucky	un + happy	unhappy
re + do	redo	re + heat	reheat
re + turn	return	re + tell	retell
non + fat	nonfat	dis + charge	discharge
non + sense	nonsense	dis + appear	disappear

ex + claim	exclaim	con + test	contest
ex + press	express	com +pound	compound
de + part	depart	com +pass	compass
de + fine	define	pre + sent	present
dis + play	display	pre + record	prerecord
dis + honor	dishonor	pre + tense	pretense

Other prefixes you will often see:
anti, tri, out, for, intro, bi, im, sub, over, and **under**

anti + body	antibody	bi + cycle	bicycle
tri + cycle	tricycle	im + print	imprint
out + doors	outdoors	sub + marine	submarine
for + get	forget	over + turn	overturn
intro +duce	introduce	under+ stood	understood